my first Number Fun BOOK

ARCTURUS

ARCTURUS

This edition published in 2019 by Arcturus Publishing Limited
26/27 Bickels Yard, 151–153 Bermondsey Street,
London SE1 3HA

Illustrator: Amanda Enright
Designer: Trudi Webb
Cover designer: Ms Mousepenny
Writer: Paul Virr

ISBN: 978-1-78950-314-2
CH007275NT
Supplier 33, Date 0519, Print run 8584

Printed in China

How to use this book

Here are some helpful hints to help you solve the puzzles.

Read the questions carefully to work out what you are being asked to do.

Always count slowly and steadily. Don't rush!

Check your answers at the back of the book, to make sure that you got everything right!

Parent's note:

This book is intended to support the learning your child does at school. You can help by encouraging your child to try all of the puzzles, even the ones they think may be difficult. Have a notebook handy so your child can write down their answers, or you may prefer to write directly into the book. Remember to have fun!

Fishy Fun

These happy fish are playing under the sea.
How many red fish are there? And how many blue fish?

How many pink and purple fish can you see?

Spider Shapes

Sally Spider has made a lovely web. How many six-sided hexagons can you find? And how many triangles?

Number Crunching!

Big Bunny ate two carrots for lunch, but how many did his friends eat? Read the clues and work it out!

I ate three more than Big Bunny.

I ate as many carrots as Big Bunny and Red bunny together!

I ate one more than Big Bunny.

I ate half the amount that Big Bunny did.

Those two carrots were yummy!

Cleaning Windows

Each worker cleans the shape of window shown on their clothes. Which one cleans the most windows?

HOME SWEET HOME

These aliens have lost their way! Help them to find home. It's the planet with the most craters.

Butterfly Spotting

Look at the spots on the wings of these pretty butterflies. Which butterflies are symmetrical?

Symmetrical means they are the same on both sides.

Building Blocks

Look at the numbers on the square blocks. How do you make the number on the roof? Do you need to add or take away the numbers below?

a

7

3   4

b

5

8   3

c

3

9   6

d

9

2   7

e

6

1   5

Elves' Workshop

Can you help these busy elves? Spot the patterns, and work out what toy each elf should make next.

All Aboard!

This train is heading home. Its home is the shed with the lowest number. Where does it belong?

START

12 – 4

6 + 2

TRICK OR TREAT?

These friends have been given 15 chocolate chews. How many treats does each child get if they are shared out equally?

Sparkly Gems

Look at these sparkly bracelets! Which bracelet would give you the most points?

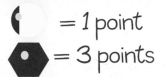

= 1 point
= 2 points
= 3 points
= 4 points

15

Moon Walk

Ready for blast off? Follow the arrows to reach your rocket safely. The numbers tell you how many squares to move in each direction.

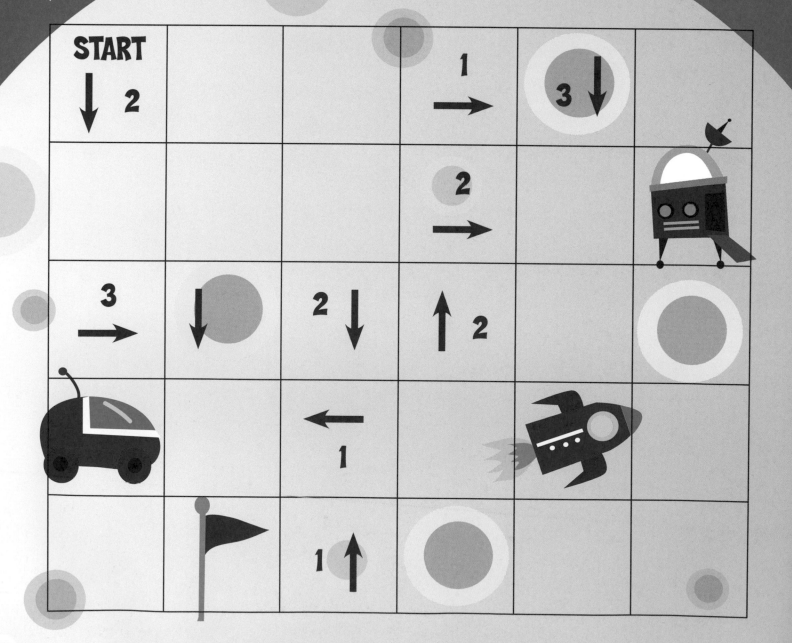

Spy School

Welcome to Spy School! Crack the code to get to your class. You need the door with the code that equals 5.

Monkey Puzzle

Help this monkey to find her way home. Her tree is the one that equals 11.

$18 - 7 = ?$

$20 - 7 = ?$

$14 - 7 = ?$

$15 - 7 = ?$

$19 - 7 = ?$

Round Town

There are so many circles in Round Town! But how many wheels can you see?

DANCE MOVES

Pattern A

20

A dancer is missing from each of these groups. What move should that dancer be performing? Can you spot the patterns?

Pattern B

Going nuts!

Fluffytail squirrel wants to share her 18 acorns equally between her three kits. How many acorns do they each get?

Answers

Page 4 Fishy Fun

There are 3 red fish, and 5 blue fish.
There are 10 pink and purple fish.

Page 5 Spider Shapes

There are 3 hexagons, and 18 triangles.

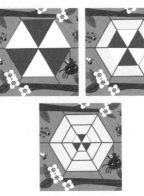

Page 6 Number Crunching!

Black Bunny ate 5 carrots.
Red Bunny ate 3 carrots.
White Bunny ate 1 carrot.
Yellow Bunny ate 5 carrots.

Page 7 Cleaning Windows

The worker cleaning the square
windows cleans the most.

Page 8 Home Sweet Home

The green planet has the most craters.

Page 9 Butterfly Spotting

Page 10 Building Blocks

a Add 3 and 4 to equal 7.
b Take away 3 from 8 to equal 5.
c Take away 6 from 9 to equal 3.
d Add 2 and 7 to equal 9.
e Add 1 and 5 to equal 6.

Page 11 Elves' Workshop

Pages 12-13 All Aboard!
The train's home is the green shed.

Page 14 Trick or Treat
Each child gets 3 chocolate chews.

Page 15 Sparkly Gems
The bracelet with 4 triangles would give you the most points.

Page 16 Moon Walk

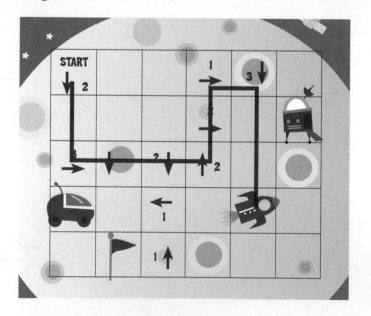

Page 17 Spy School
The green door adds up to 5

Page 18 Monkey Puzzle

Page 19 Round Town
There are 8 wheels in the picture.

Pages 20-21 Dance Moves

Page 22 Going Nuts!
They each get 6 acorns.